SCALES, CHORDS & ARPEGGIOS

BY JAMES BASTIEN

KJOS NEIL A. KJOS MUSIC COMPANY • SAN DIEGO, CALIFORNIA

PREFACE

This book provides all the major, harmonic and melodic minor scales, arpeggios, and cadence patterns using root position and inversions. These materials may be used for study and for auditions such as those sponsored by the National Guild of Piano Teachers. When the scales, chords, and arpeggios are practiced regularly, the student's facility at the keyboard will improve.

The relative major and minor scales are on facing pages for easy reference. The melodic minor scales begin on page 34.

These scales may be used for systematic study beginning as early as *Level 2* of **Bastien Piano Basics** and continuing through *Level 4*. This book may also be used with any other piano method at similar levels.

We offer you our best wishes for success with *Scales, Chords and Arpeggios*.

Neil A. Kjos Music Company
James Bastien
Jane Smisor Bastien

CONTENTS

ISBN 0-8497-9351-3

C Major

Scales

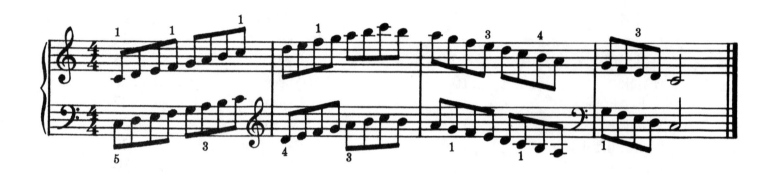

Cadence Patterns

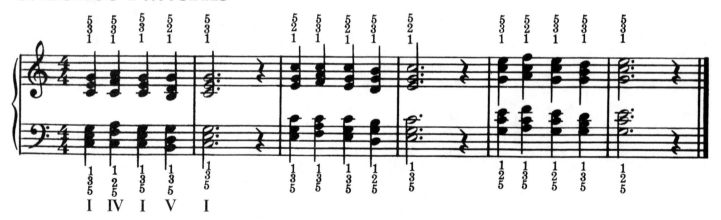

I   IV   I   V   I

Arpeggios

A Harmonic Minor

Scales

Cadence Patterns

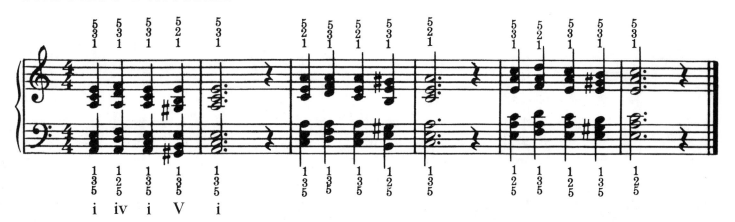

i   iv   i   V   i

Arpeggios

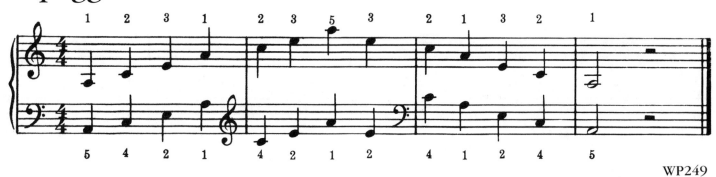

G Major

Scales

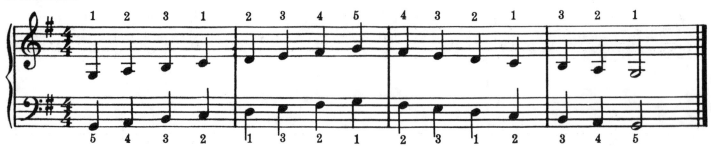

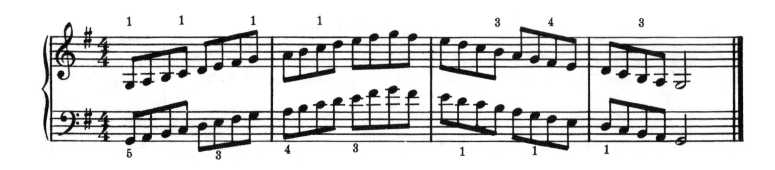

Cadence Patterns

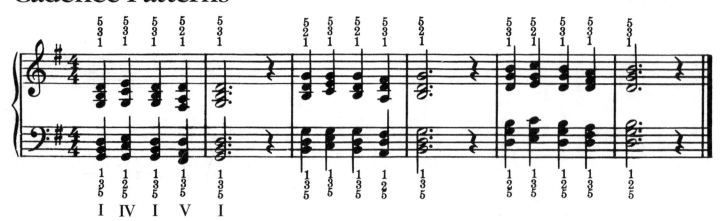

I IV I V I

Arpeggios

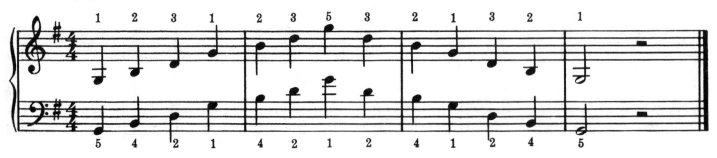

E Harmonic Minor

Scales

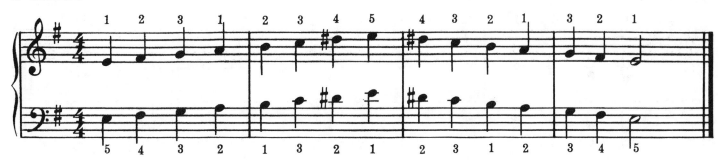

Cadence Patterns

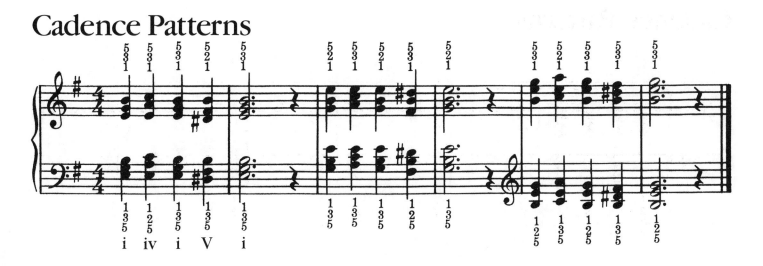

i   iv   i   V   i

Arpeggios

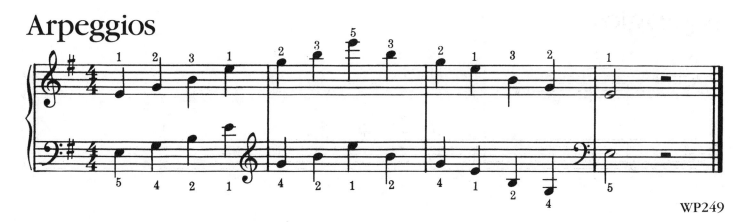

D Major

Scales

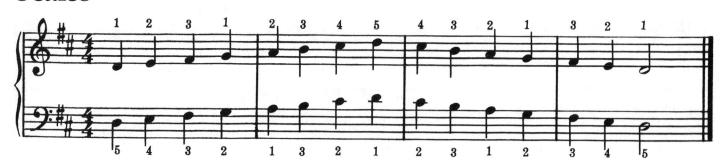

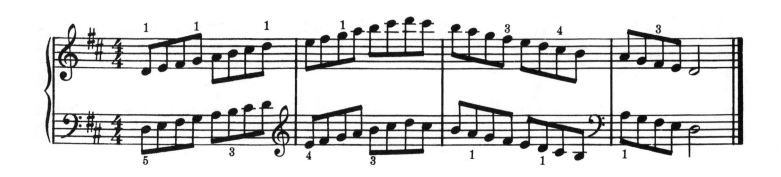

Cadence Patterns

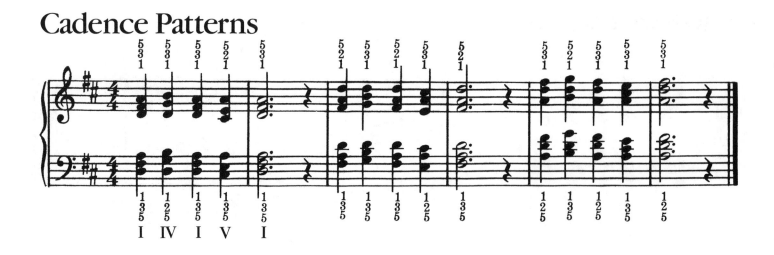

I IV I V I

Arpeggios

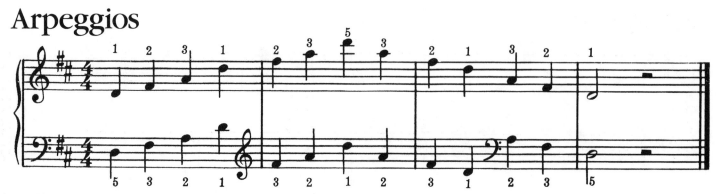

B Harmonic Minor

Scales

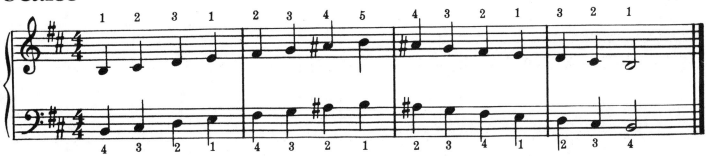

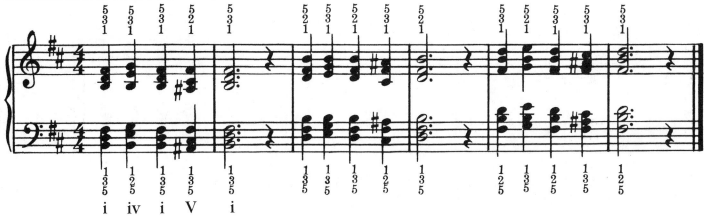

Cadence Patterns

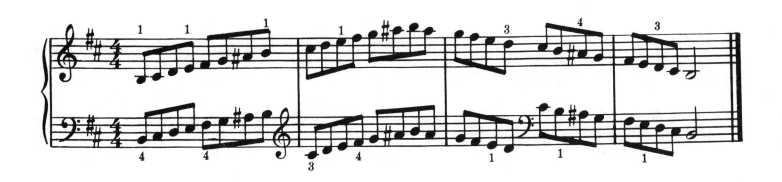

i   iv   i   V   i

Arpeggios

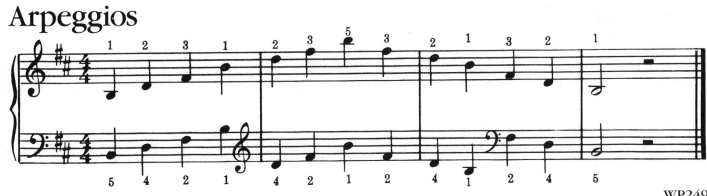

A Major

Scales

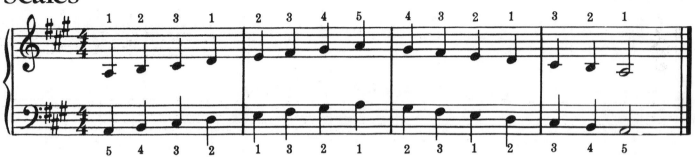

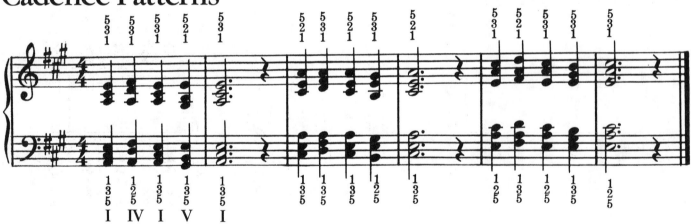

Cadence Patterns

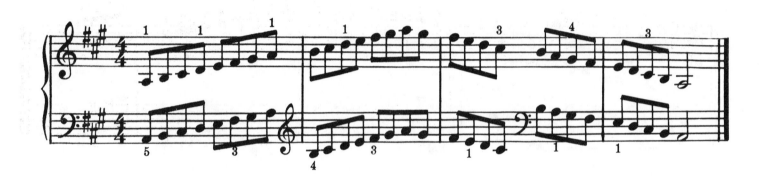

I IV I V I

Arpeggios

F♯ Harmonic Minor

Scales

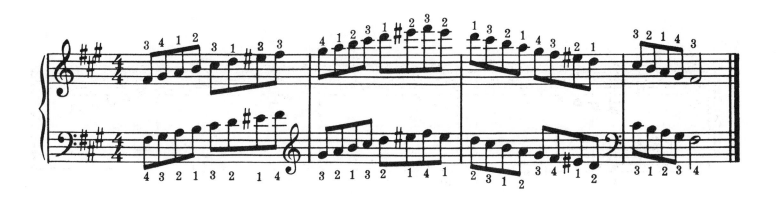

Cadence Patterns

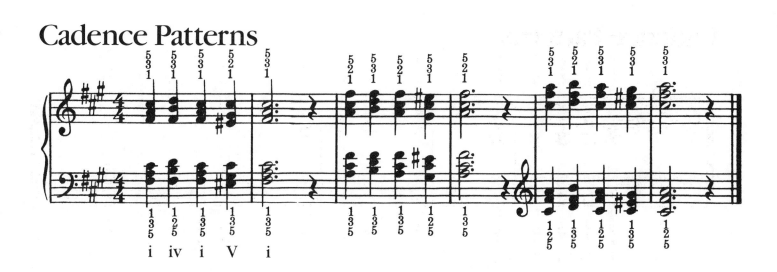

i iv i V i

Arpeggios

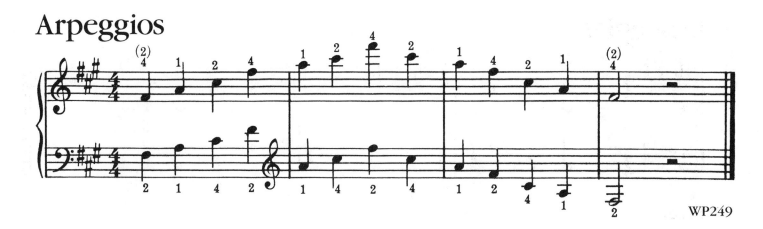

E Major

Scales

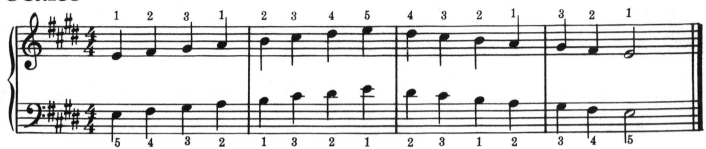

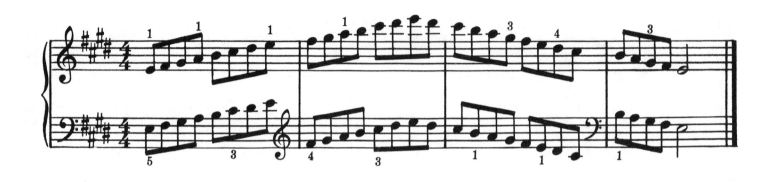

Cadence Patterns

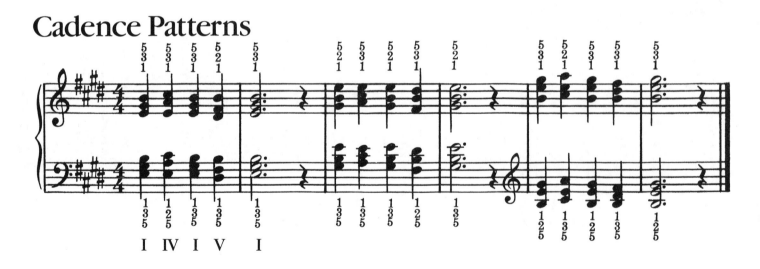

I IV I V I

Arpeggios

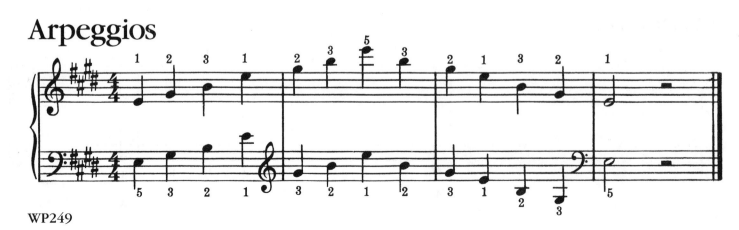

C# Harmonic Minor

Scales

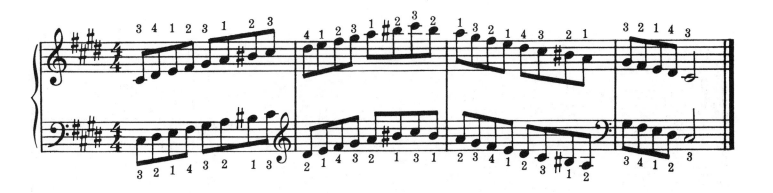

Cadence Patterns

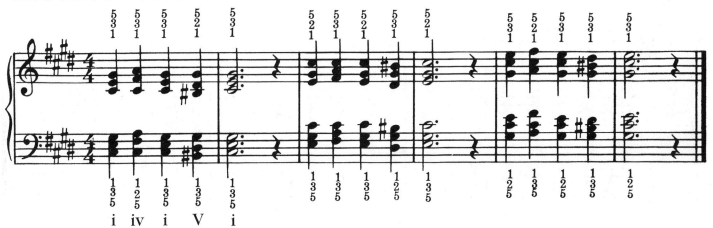

i iv i V i

Arpeggios

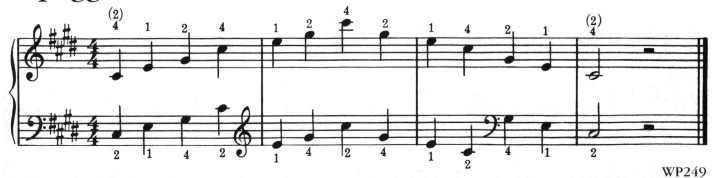

B Major

Scales

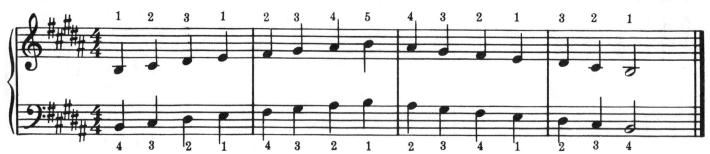

Cadence Patterns

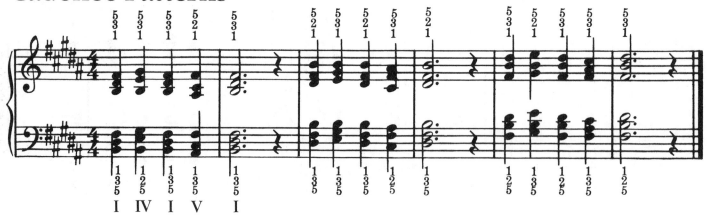

Arpeggios

G♯ Harmonic Minor

Scales

Double sharp: raises note a whole step.

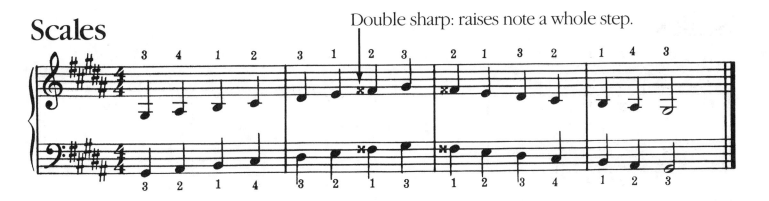

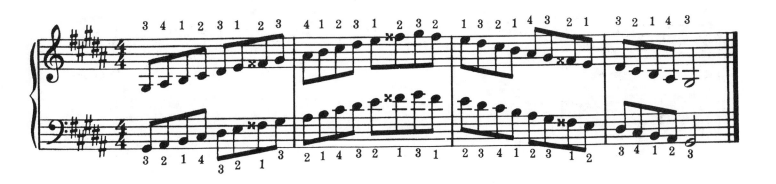

Cadence Patterns

i iv i V i

Arpeggios

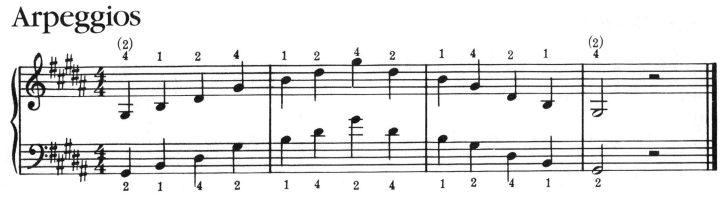

F♯ Major

Scales

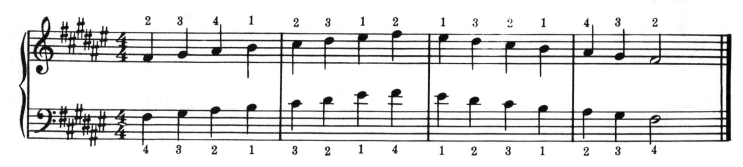

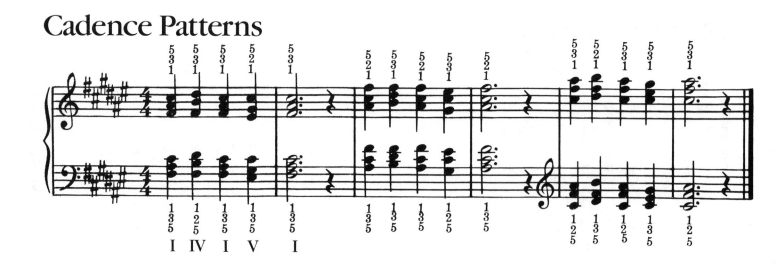

Cadence Patterns

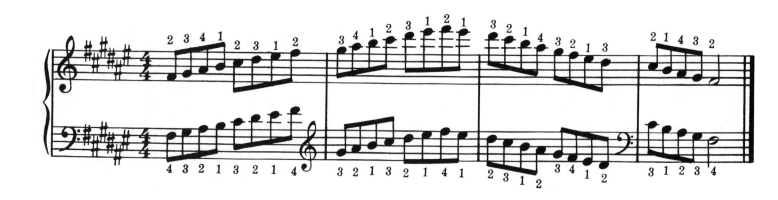

I   IV   I   V   I

Arpeggios

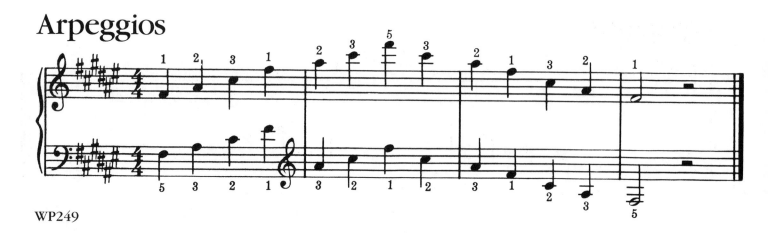

D♯ Harmonic Minor

Scales

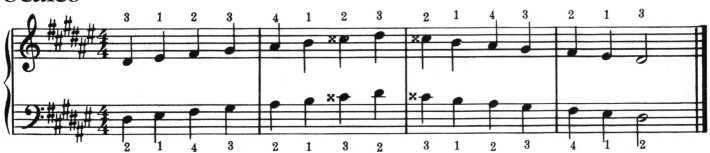

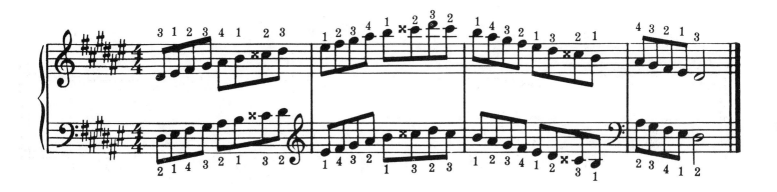

Cadence Patterns

i   iv   i   V   i

Arpeggios

C# Major

Scales

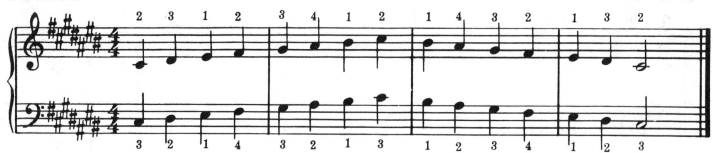

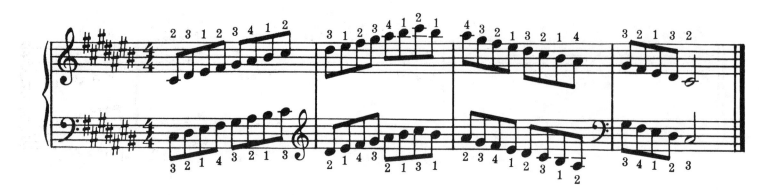

Cadence Patterns

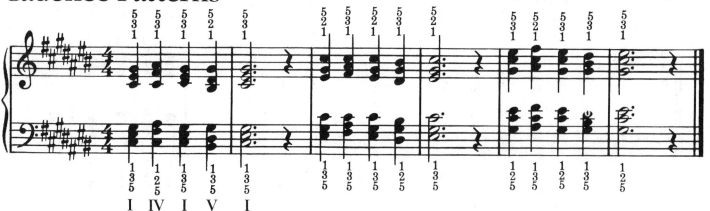

I IV I V I

Arpeggios

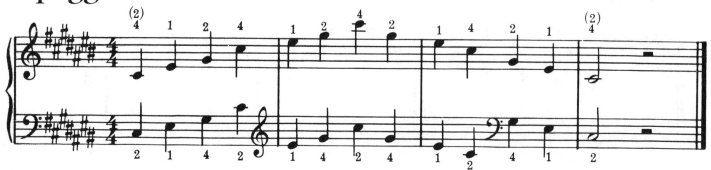

A♯ Harmonic Minor

Scales

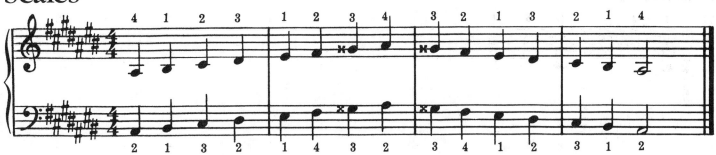

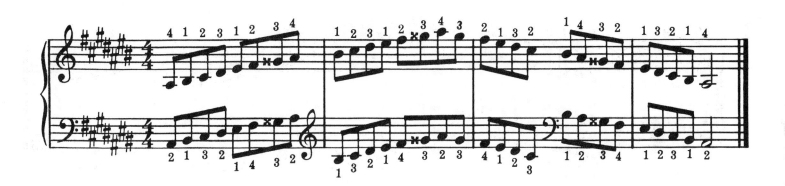

Cadence Patterns

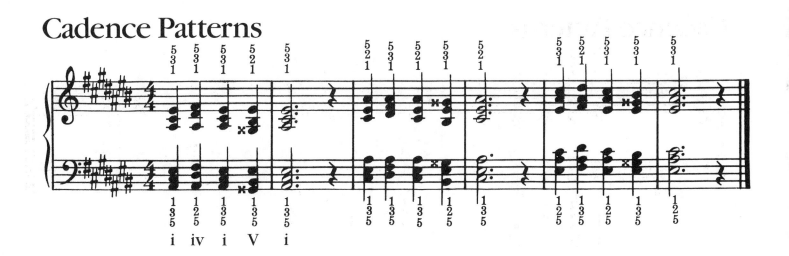

i iv i V i

Arpeggios

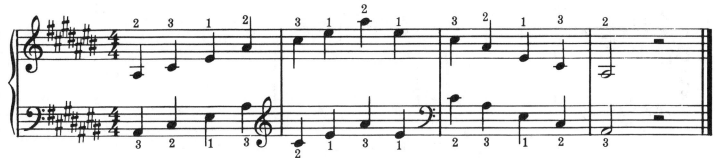

F Major

Scales

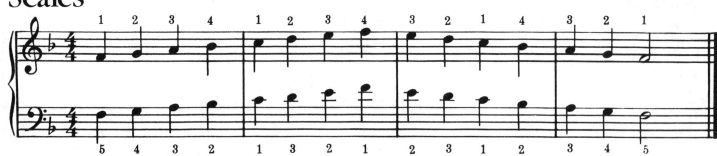

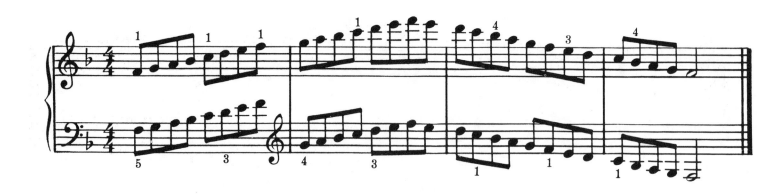

Cadence Patterns

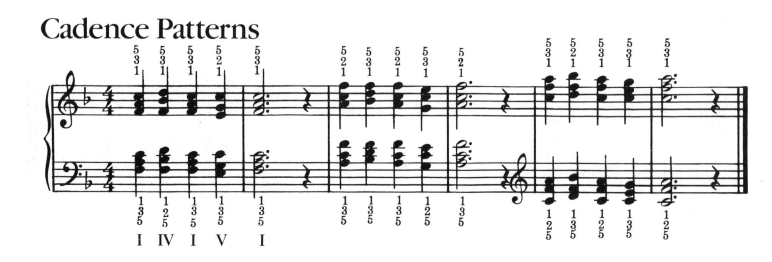

I IV I V I

Arpeggios

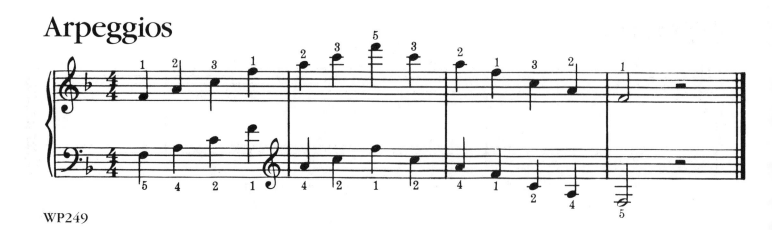

D Harmonic Minor

Scales

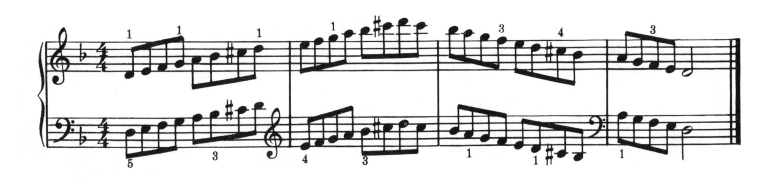

Cadence Patterns

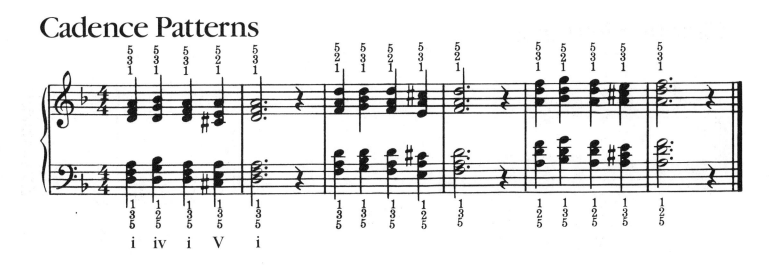

i   iv   i   V   i

Arpeggios

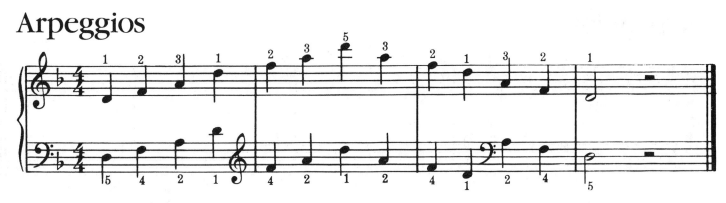

B♭ Major

Scales

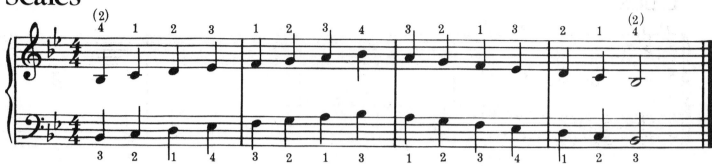

Cadence Patterns

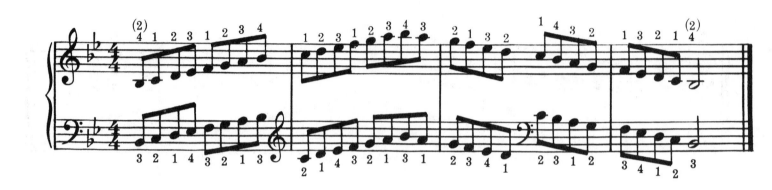

I   IV   I   V   I

Arpeggios

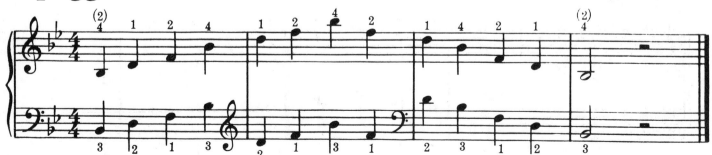

G Harmonic Minor

Scales

Cadence Patterns

i iv i V i

Arpeggios

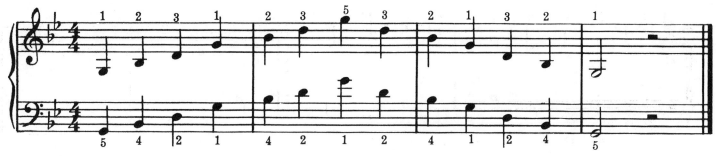

E♭ Major

Scales

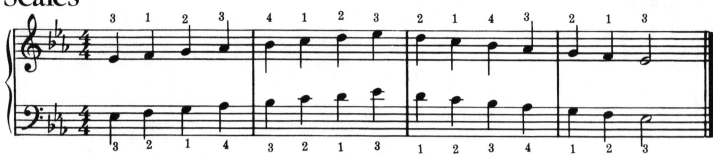

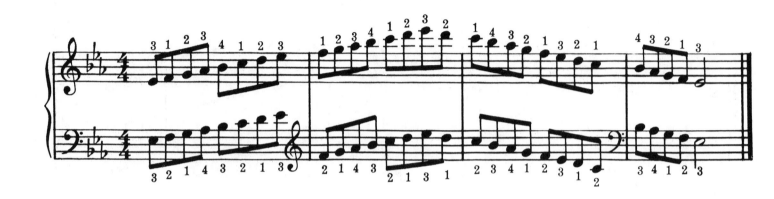

Cadence Patterns

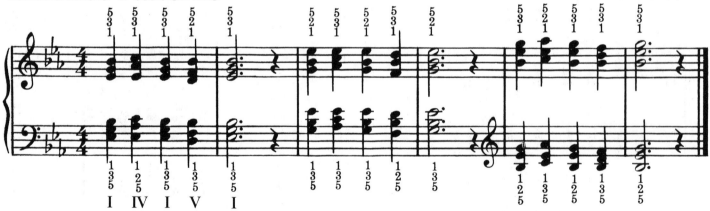

I   IV   I   V   I

Arpeggios

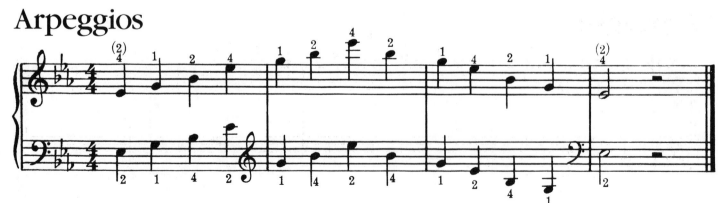

C Harmonic Minor

Scales

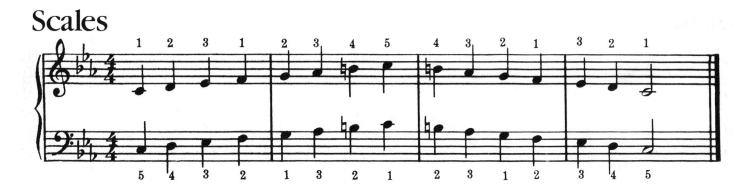

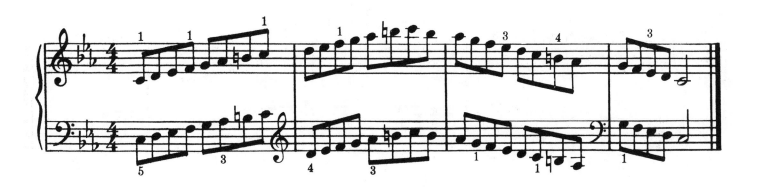

Cadence Patterns

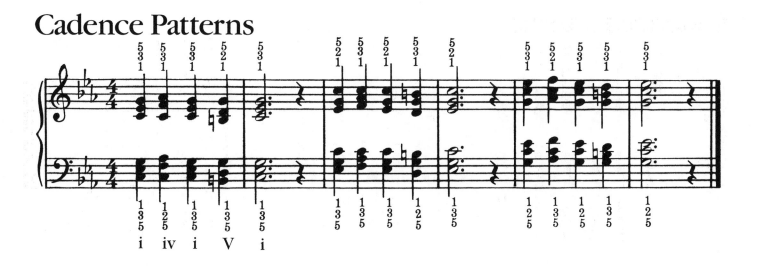

i   iv   i   V   i

Arpeggios

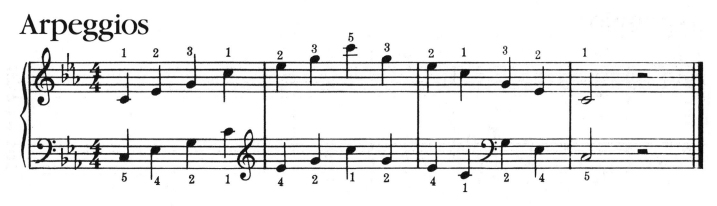

A♭ Major

Scales

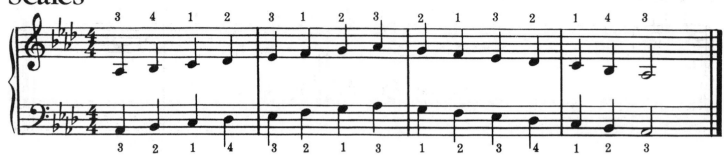

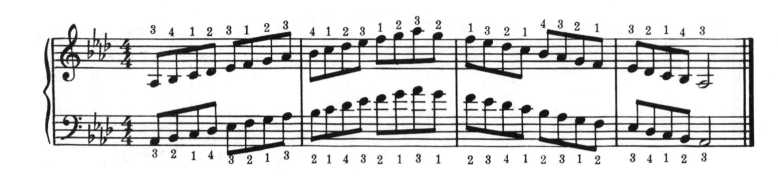

Cadence Patterns

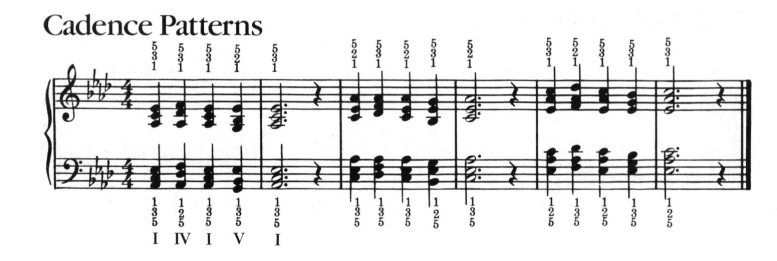

I   IV   I   V   I

Arpeggios

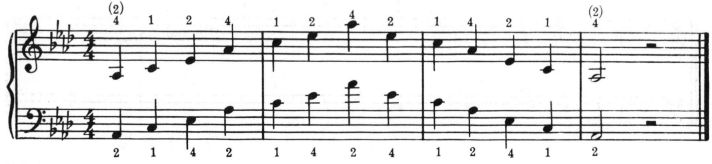

F Harmonic Minor

Scales

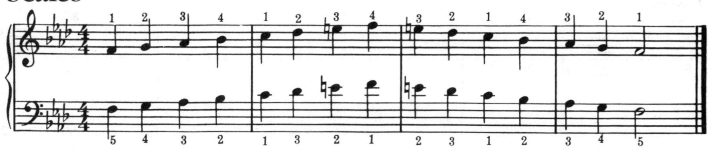

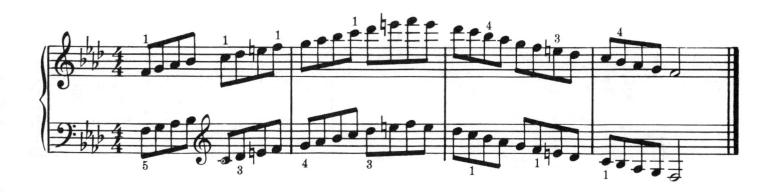

Cadence Patterns

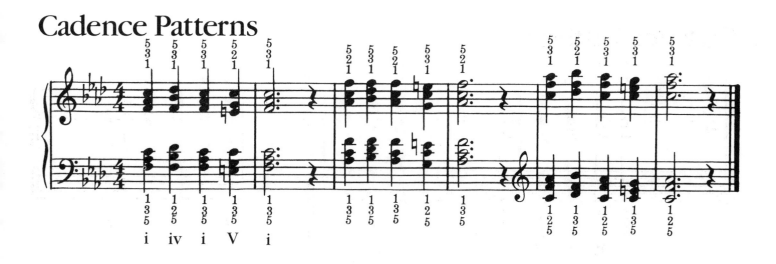

i   iv   i   V   i

Arpeggios

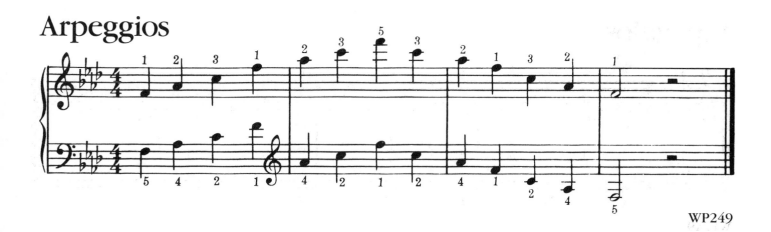

D♭ Major

Scales

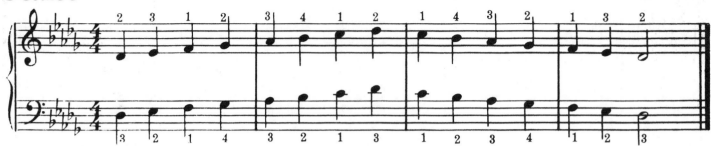

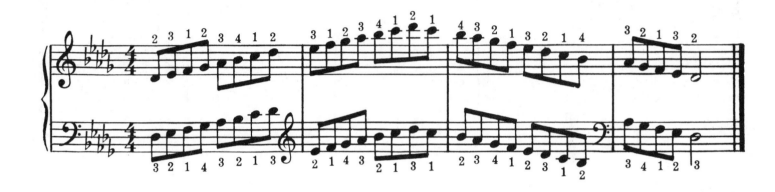

Cadence Patterns

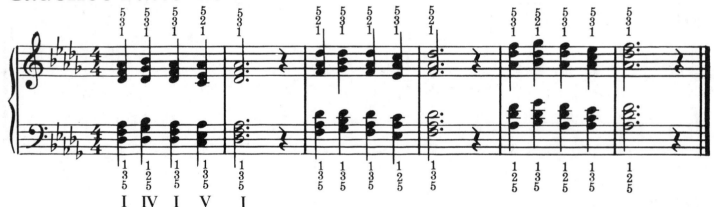

I IV I V I

Arpeggios

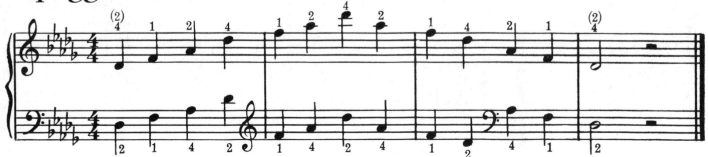

B♭ Harmonic Minor

Scales

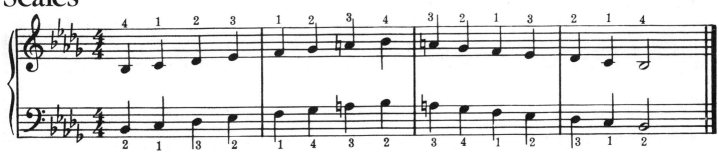

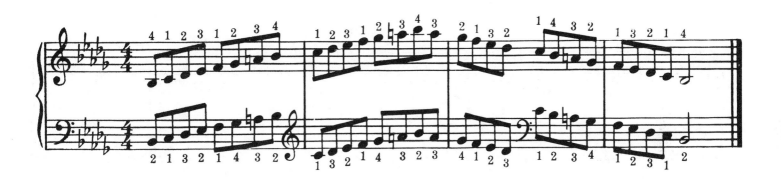

Cadence Patterns

i iv i V i

Arpeggios

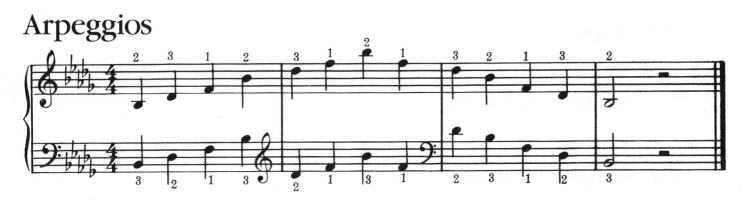

G♭ Major

Scales

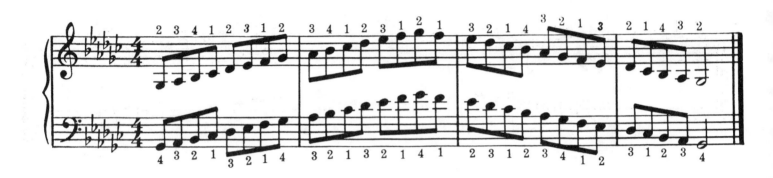

Cadence Patterns

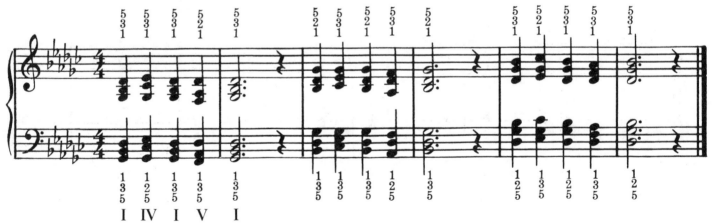

I   IV   I   V   I

Arpeggios

E♭ Harmonic Minor

Scales

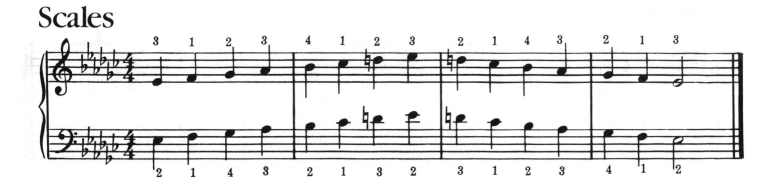

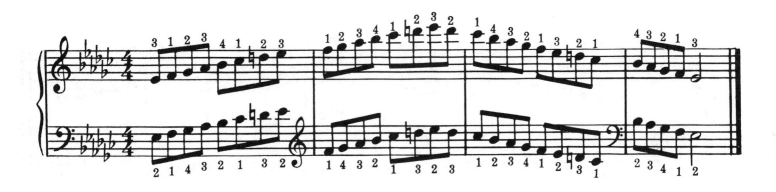

Cadence Patterns

i   iv   i   V   i

Arpeggios

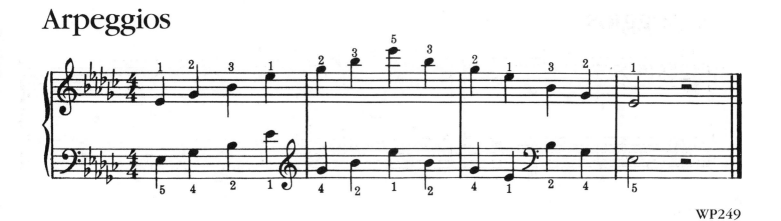

C♭ Major

Scales

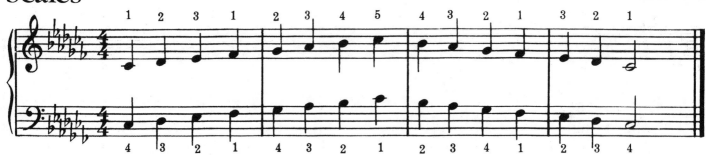

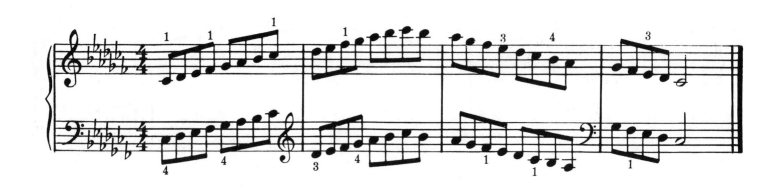

Cadence Patterns

I   IV   I   V   I

Arpeggios

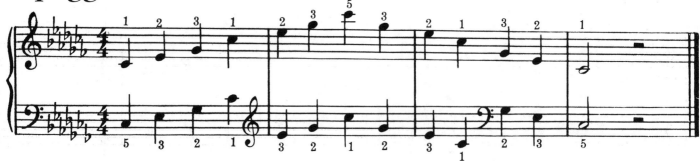

A♭ Harmonic Minor

Scales

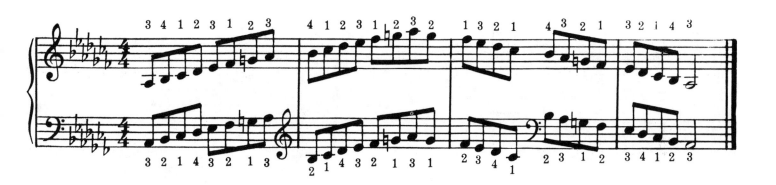

Cadence Patterns

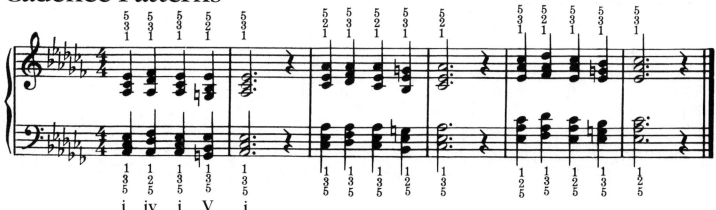

i   iv   i   V   i

Arpeggios

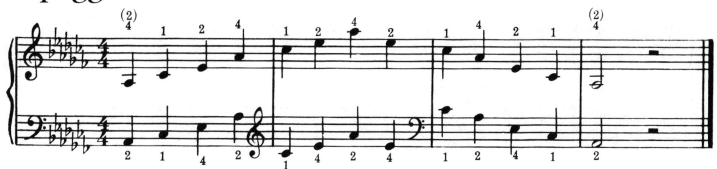

Melodic Minor Scales

A (relative to C Major)

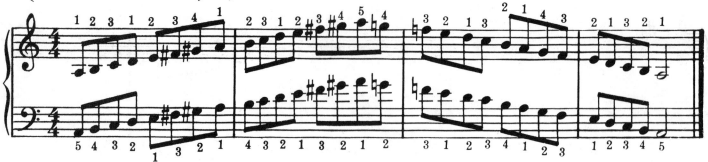

E (relative to G Major)

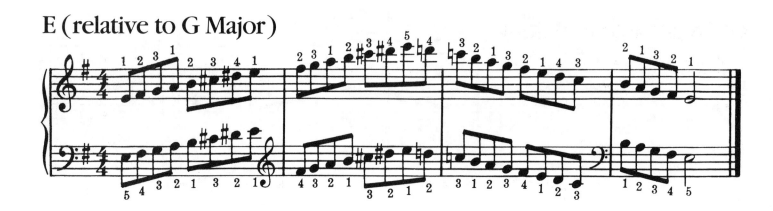

B (relative to D Major)

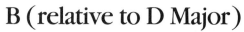

F♯ (relative to A Major)

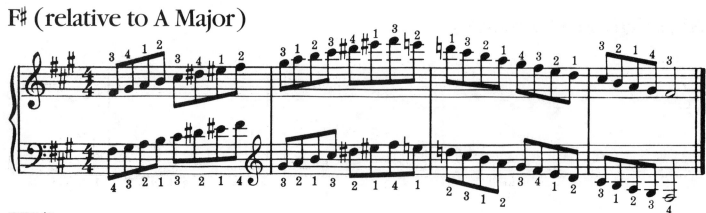

C# (relative to E Major)

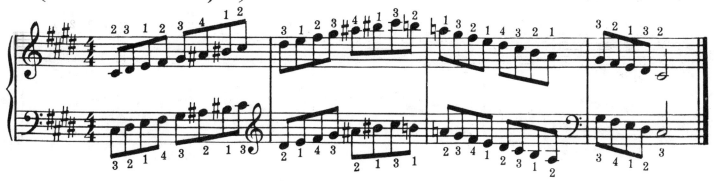

G# (relative to B Major)

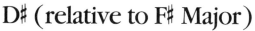
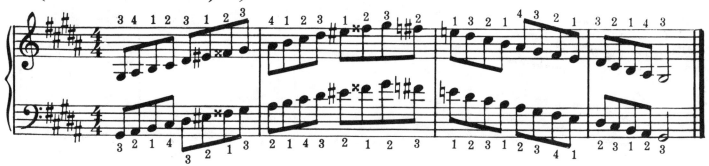

D# (relative to F# Major)

A# (relative to C# Major)

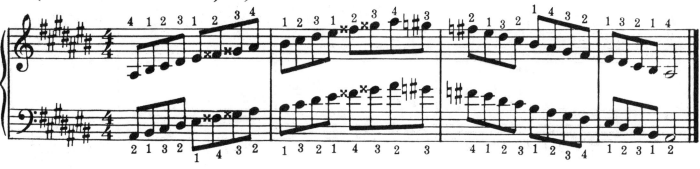

D (relative to F Major)

G (relative to B♭ Major)

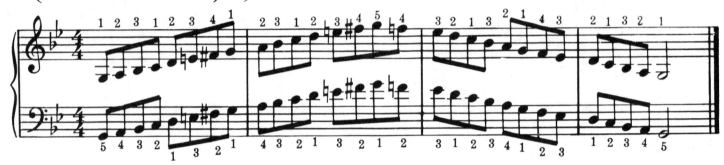

C (relative to E♭ Major)

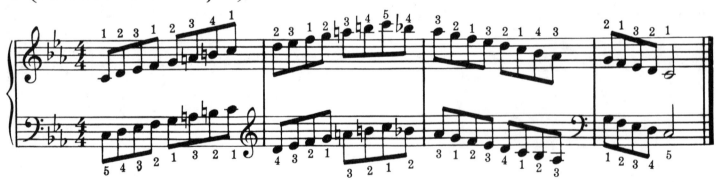

F (relative to A♭ Major)

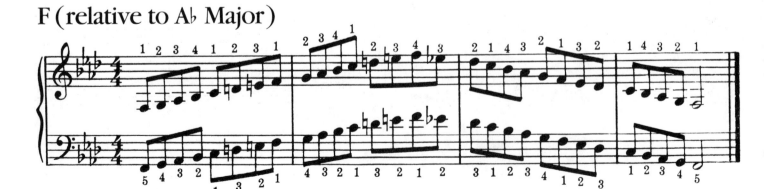

B♭ (relative to D♭ Major)

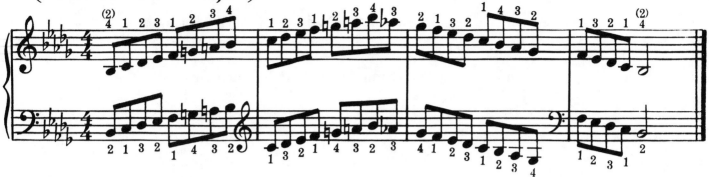

E♭ (relative to G♭ Major)

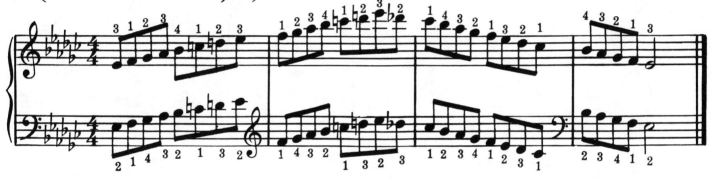

A♭ (relative to C♭ Major)

Circle of 5ths

This chart is called the **circle of 5ths**. The sharps are arranged from the top, moving clockwise. The flats are arranged from the top, moving counterclockwise.

There are fifteen Major keys: seven sharp keys, seven flat keys, and one key with no sharps or flats.

Similarly, there are fifteen relative minor keys.

The keys at the bottom of the circle are called **enharmonic**. They each have **two** names.

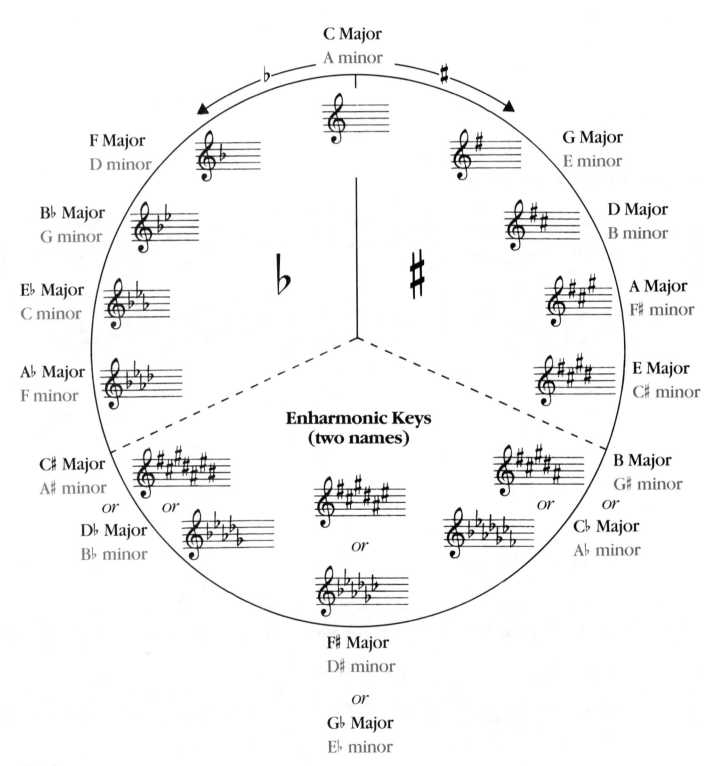

Chord Dictionary